Created by
Marilyn Burns

D1303417

Multiplication Ⓑ

Facts through 12 × 12

WorkSpace

Cover photo: © Mark Scott/Getty Images, insert: © David Madison/Getty Images

Printed in the U.S.A.

ISBN 978-0-545-01004-7

18   19   20   21   22   23   24   25   26   11945   26   25   24   23   22   21   20   19   18

4510004291

v.B

Equal Rows

1

$$3 \times 5 = 15$$

Write a multiplication equation for the group of tiles.

2

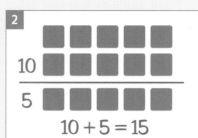

$$10 + 5 = 15$$

Explain with words, pictures, or numbers how you figured the number of tiles without counting them.

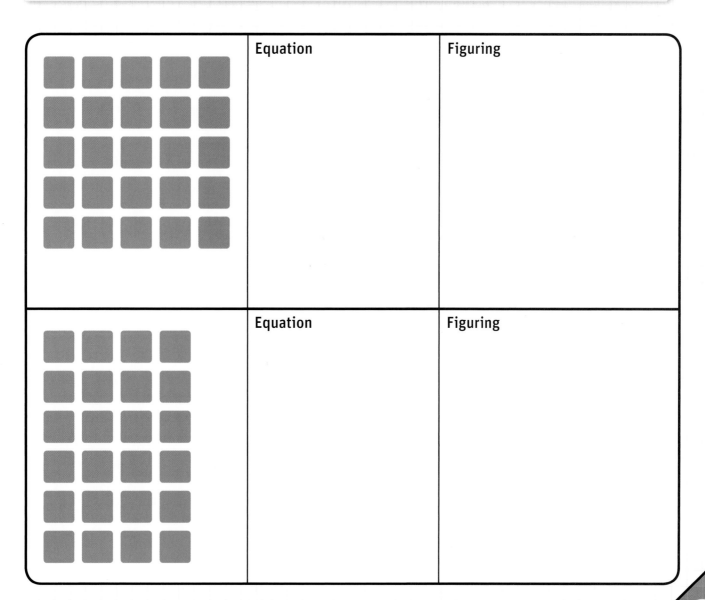

	Equation	Figuring
	Equation	Figuring

Home Note: Your child writes multiplication equations for equal rows.

Lesson 1 · 1

Game Rules for Tiles Capture

What you need

- *Tiles Capture* cards, 9 for each player
- *WorkSpace* pages 3 and 4 or blank paper
- pencil

➤ **Each turn has three steps.**

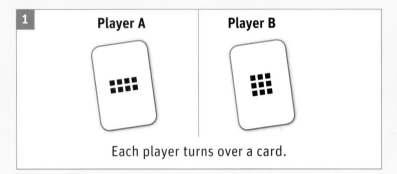

1

Player A   **Player B**

Each player turns over a card.

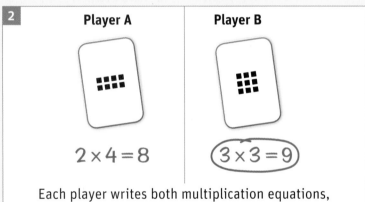

2

Player A   **Player B**

$2 \times 4 = 8$ $\left(3 \times 3 = 9\right)$

Each player writes both multiplication equations, and circles the equation with the greater product.

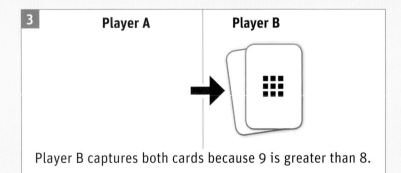

3

Player A   **Player B**

Player B captures both cards because 9 is greater than 8.

➤ **When all the cards have been played, the winner is the player with the most cards.**

Home Note: Your child practices multiplying factors 1–6 by playing a game.

Tiles Capture

HOW TO PLAY

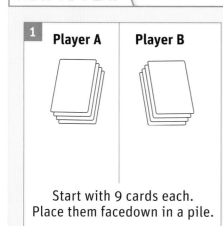

1   Player A   Player B

Start with 9 cards each. Place them facedown in a pile.

2   Player A   Player B

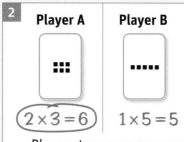

$2 \times 3 = 6$ $1 \times 5 = 5$

Players turn over one card each, write both multiplication equations, and circle the equation with the greater product.

3   Player A   Player B

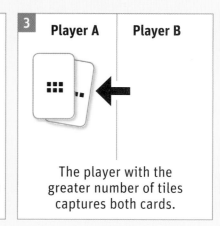

The player with the greater number of tiles captures both cards.

Player A	Player B

Home Note: Your child practices multiplying factors 1–6 by playing a game.

Tiles Capture

HOW TO PLAY

1 | Player A | Player B

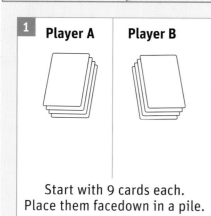

Start with 9 cards each.
Place them facedown in a pile.

2 | Player A | Player B

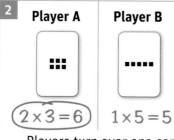

$2 \times 3 = 6$ | $1 \times 5 = 5$

Players turn over one card
each, write both multiplication
equations, and circle the equation
with the greater product.

3 | Player A | Player B

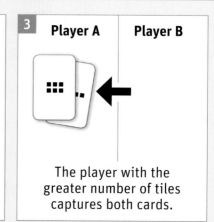

The player with the
greater number of tiles
captures both cards.

Player A	Player B

Home Note: Your child practices multiplying factors 1–6 by playing a game.

Multiplication Chart

X	1	2	3	4	5	6	7	8	9	10	11	12
1	1	2	3	4	5	6	7	8	9	10	11	12
2	2	4	6	8	10	12	14	16	18	20	22	24
3	3	6	9	12	15	18	21	24	27	30	33	36
4	4	8	12	16	20	24	28	32	36	40	44	48
5	5	10	15	20	25	30	35	40	45	50	55	60
6	6	12	18	24	30	36	42	48	54	60	66	72
7	7	14	21	28	35	42	49	56	63	70	77	84
8	8	16	24	32	40	48	56	64	72	80	88	96
9	9	18	27	36	45	54	63	72	81	90	99	108
10	10	20	30	40	50	60	70	80	90	100	110	120
11	11	22	33	44	55	66	77	88	99	110	121	132
12	12	24	36	48	60	72	84	96	108	120	132	144

Home Note: Your child uses the multiplication chart to find products with factors through 12 × 12.

Find Products on the Multiplication Chart

DIRECTIONS

> Use the multiplication chart to find each product.

X	1	2	3	4	5	6	7	8	9	10	11	12
1	1	2	3	4	5	6	7	8	9	10	11	12
2	2	4	6	8	10	12	14	16	18	20	22	24
3	3	6	9	12	15	18	21	24	27	30	33	36
4	4	8	12	16	20	24	28	32	36	40	44	48
5	5	10	15	20	25	30	35	40	45	50	55	60
6	6	12	18	24	30	36	42	48	54	60	66	72
7	7	14	21	28	35	42	49	56	63	70	77	84
8	8	16	24	32	40	48	56	64	72	80	88	96
9	9	18	27	36	45	54	63	72	81	90	99	108
10	10	20	30	40	50	60	70	80	90	100	110	120
11	11	22	33	44	55	66	77	88	99	110	121	132
12	12	24	36	48	60	72	84	96	108	120	132	144

① $5 \times 7 =$ ☐

② $6 \times 10 =$ ☐

③ $8 \times 8 =$ ☐

④ $4 \times 7 =$ ☐

⑤ $3 \times 9 =$ ☐

⑥ $2 \times 12 =$ ☐

⑦ $9 \times 9 =$ ☐

⑧ $6 \times 7 =$ ☐

⑨ $1 \times 11 =$ ☐

⑩ $12 \times 9 =$ ☐

⑪ $10 \times 10 =$ ☐

⑫ $5 \times 12 =$ ☐

Home Note: Your child uses a multiplication chart to find products with factors through 12×12.

Rectangles Built with 12 Tiles

➤ Draw rectangles on the grid as your teacher instructs.

➤ Label the sides of each rectangle.

➤ Write an equation inside each rectangle.

Home Note: Your child draws rectangles and writes equations for them.

Show What You Know

DIRECTIONS

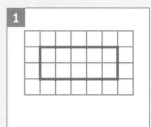

1 Draw each rectangle you build with 10 tiles.

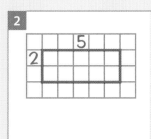

2 Label the rectangle.

3 Write an equation in the rectangle.

4 Color the square that would cover the product if you placed the rectangle on the chart.

Here is an example with 8 tiles.

	4										
2	2 × 4 = 8										

Home Note: Your child draws rectangles and writes equations for them.

Write Products and Factors

➤ Write the products.

➤ You may use the multiplication chart to find or check your answers.

X	1	2	3	4	5	6	7	8	9	10	11	12
1	1	2	3	4	5	6	7	8	9	10	11	12
2	2	4	6	8	10	12	14	16	18	20	22	24
3	3	6	9	12	15	18	21	24	27	30	33	36
4	4	8	12	16	20	24	28	32	36	40	44	48
5	5	10	15	20	25	30	35	40	45	50	55	60
6	6	12	18	24	30	36	42	48	54	60	66	72
7	7	14	21	28	35	42	49	56	63	70	77	84
8	8	16	24	32	40	48	56	64	72	80	88	96
9	9	18	27	36	45	54	63	72	81	90	99	108
10	10	20	30	40	50	60	70	80	90	100	110	120
11	11	22	33	44	55	66	77	88	99	110	121	132
12	12	24	36	48	60	72	84	96	108	120	132	144

1. $8 \times 6 =$ ☐

2. $2 \times 9 =$ ☐

3. $3 \times 8 =$ ☐

4. $9 \times 9 =$ ☐

5. $11 \times 4 =$ ☐

6. $5 \times 10 =$ ☐

7. $8 \times 8 =$ ☐

8. $12 \times 10 =$ ☐

9. $6 \times 6 =$ ☐

10. $5 \times 3 =$ ☐

11. $7 \times 4 =$ ☐

12. $10 \times 3 =$ ☐

13. $9 \times 8 =$ ☐

14. $6 \times 5 =$ ☐

15. $2 \times 12 =$ ☐

Home Note: Your child writes products in equations.

Tiles Capture

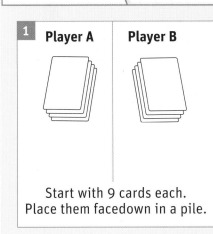

1 Player A | Player B

Start with 9 cards each.
Place them facedown in a pile.

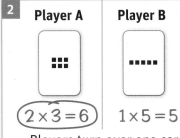

2 Player A | Player B

$2 \times 3 = 6$ $1 \times 5 = 5$

Players turn over one card
each, write both multiplication
equations, and circle the equation
with the greater product.

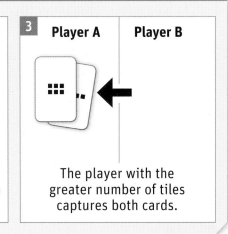

3 Player A | Player B

The player with the
greater number of tiles
captures both cards.

Player A	Player B

Home Note: Your child practices multiplying factors 1–6 by playing a game.

Missing Products Chart

X	1	2	3	4	5	6	7	8	9	10	11	12
1												
2												
3												
4												
5												
6												
7												
8												
9												
10												
11												
12												

Home Note: Your child writes products on a missing-products chart.

Rectangles Built with 9 tiles

DIRECTIONS

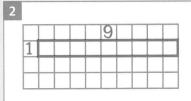

1 Draw each rectangle you build with 9 tiles.

2 Label the rectangle.

3 Write an equation in the rectangle.

Home Note: Your child draws rectangles and writes equations for them.

Lesson 6

13

Multiplication Chart

X	1	2	3	4	5	6	7	8	9	10	11	12
1	1	2	3	4	5	6	7	8	9	10	11	12
2	2	4	6	8	10	12	14	16	18	20	22	24
3	3	6	9	12	15	18	21	24	27	30	33	36
4	4	8	12	16	20	24	28	32	36	40	44	48
5	5	10	15	20	25	30	35	40	45	50	55	60
6	6	12	18	24	30	36	42	48	54	60	66	72
7	7	14	21	28	35	42	49	56	63	70	77	84
8	8	16	24	32	40	48	56	64	72	80	88	96
9	9	18	27	36	45	54	63	72	81	90	99	108
10	10	20	30	40	50	60	70	80	90	100	110	120
11	11	22	33	44	55	66	77	88	99	110	121	132
12	12	24	36	48	60	72	84	96	108	120	132	144

Home Note: Your child verifies products on a multiplication chart.

Making Rectangles

1 Build a rectangle with your tiles.

2 Draw the rectangle on the grid on page 17.

3 Write an equation inside the rectangle.

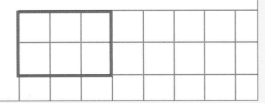

$2 \times 3 = 6$

4 Cut out your rectangle.

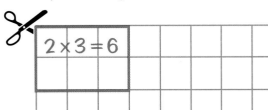

$2 \times 3 = 6$

5 Write the product on your missing-products chart on page 12.

X	1	2	3	4	5	6	7	8
1								
2			6					

16 Lesson 7

Home Note: Your child reads directions for making rectangles.

Rectangles for Your Number

1 Our number is ___10___ .

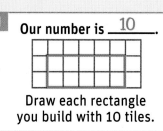

Draw each rectangle
you build with 10 tiles.

2

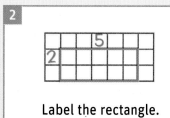

Label the rectangle.

3

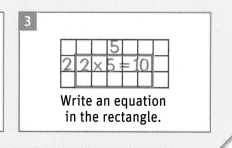

Write an equation
in the rectangle.

Our number is _____ .

Home Note: Your child draws rectangles and writes equations for them.

Grid Paper

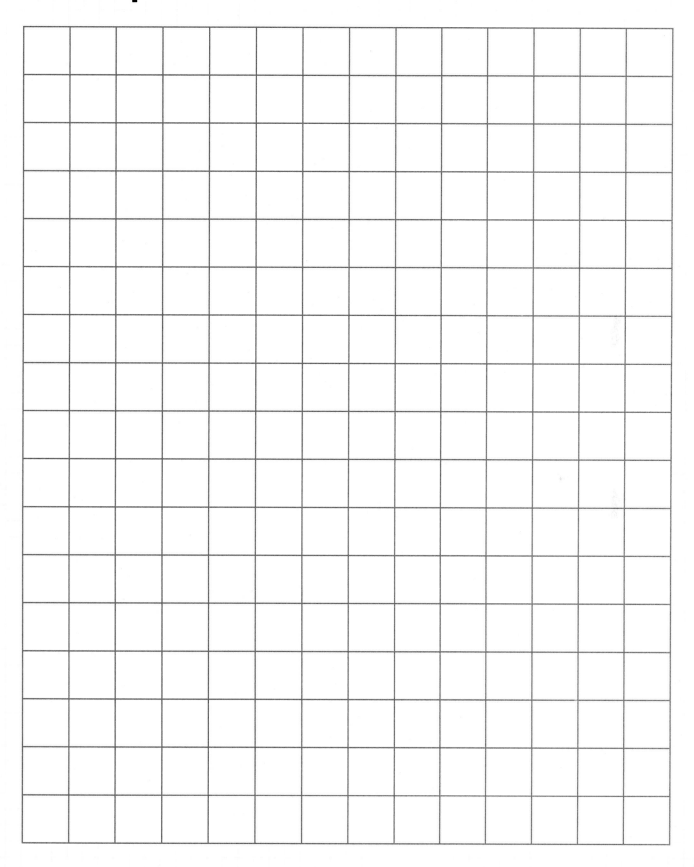

Home Note: Your child draws rectangles and writes equations for them.

Draw Rectangles and Figure Out Products

➤ Draw a rectangle for each multiplication problem below.

➤ Refer to the directions on page 16, if necessary.

➤ Write the product for each rectangle on your missing-products chart on page 12.

8 × 4   10 × 6   9 × 5

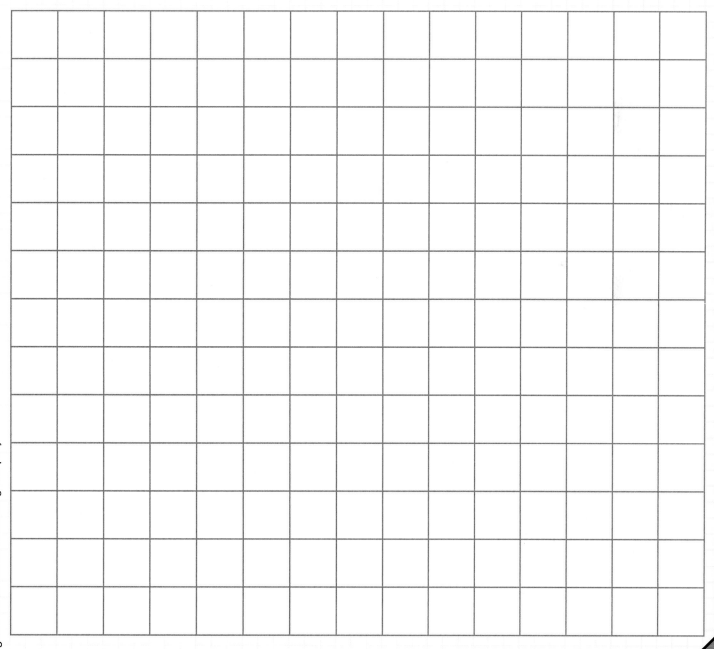

Home Note: Your child draws rectangles and writes equations for them.

Making Rectangles

1 Figure out how many rows and how many in each row your rectangle will have.

2×3
can be read as
2 rows of 3.

2 Draw the rectangle on the grid on page 25.

3 Write an equation inside the rectangle.

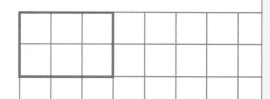

$2 \times 3 = 6$

4 Cut out your rectangle.

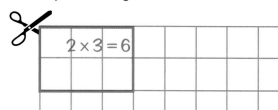

$2 \times 3 = 6$

5 Write the product on the Missing Products chart on page 12.

X	1	2	3	4	5	6	7	8
1								
2			6					

6 Turn the rectangle and write a second equation.

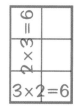

$2 \times 3 = 6$

$3 \times 2 = 6$

7 Write the product on the Missing Products chart on page 12.

X	1	2	3	4	5	6	7	8
1								
2			6					
3		6						
4								
5								

Home Note: Your child reads directions for making rectangles.

Draw Rectangles and Figure Out Products

DIRECTIONS

➤ Draw a rectangle for the multiplication problem you chose.

➤ Refer to the directions on page 23, if necessary.

➤ Write the product on the Missing Products chart on page 12.

➤ Turn the rectangle and write a second equation.

➤ Write the product on the Missing Products chart on page 12.

Home Note: Your child draws rectangles and writes equations for them.

Grid Paper

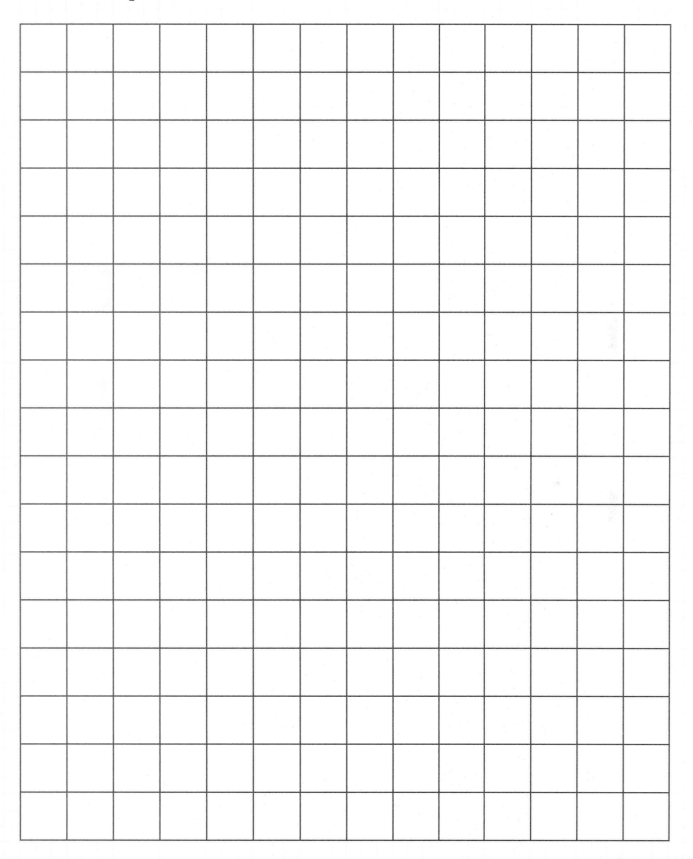

Home Note: Your child draws rectangles and writes equations for them.

Show What You Know

➤ For each rectangle below, write a multiplication equation.

①

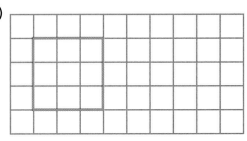

Multiplication equation _____

②

Multiplication equation _____

③

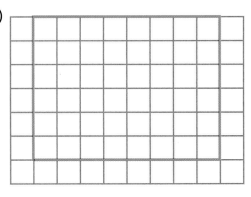

Multiplication equation _____

④

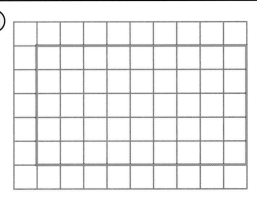

Multiplication equation _____

Home Note: Your child writes equations for rectangles.

Show What You Know

DIRECTIONS

➤ Draw a rectangle for each multiplication problem.
➤ Write an equation for each.

① 2 × 6

Equation _____

② 4 × 4

Equation _____

③ 5 × 8

Equation _____

④ 6 × 9

Equation _____

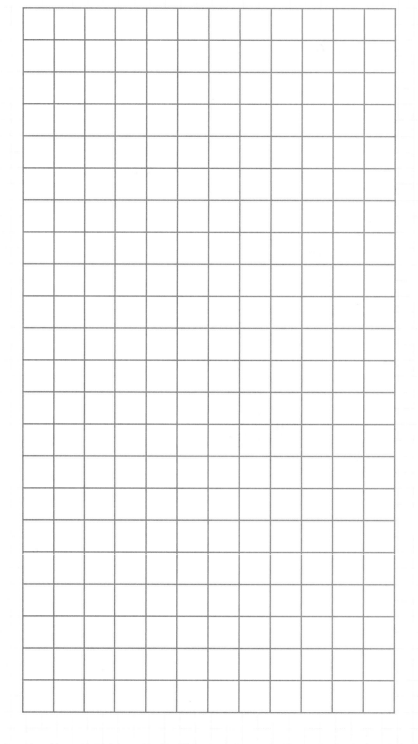

⑤ 3 × 10

Equation _____

⑥ 7 × 4

Equation _____

⑦ 5 × 8

Equation _____

⑧ 8 × 7

Equation _____

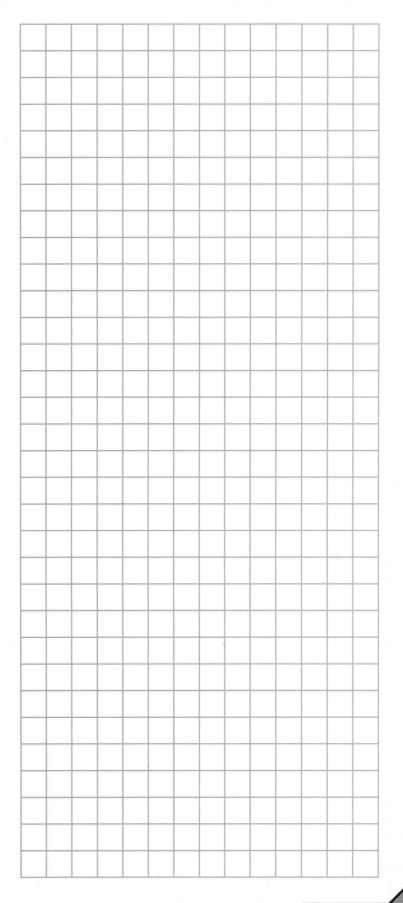

Home Note: Your child draws rectangles and writes equations for multiplication problems.

Tiles Capture

HOW TO PLAY

1   **Player A**   **Player B**

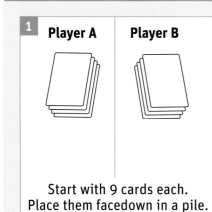

Start with 9 cards each.
Place them facedown in a pile.

2   **Player A**   **Player B**

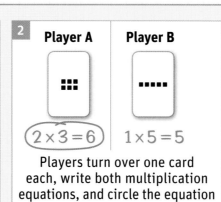

$2 \times 3 = 6$ $1 \times 5 = 5$

Players turn over one card
each, write both multiplication
equations, and circle the equation
with the greater product.

3   **Player A**   **Player B**

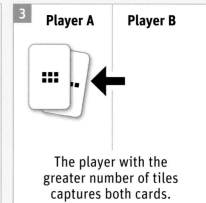

The player with the
greater number of tiles
captures both cards.

Player A	Player B

Home Note: Your child practices multiplying factors 1–6 by playing a game.

Growing Pattern of 6s

DIRECTIONS

➤ Your teacher will tell you what to draw on the grid.

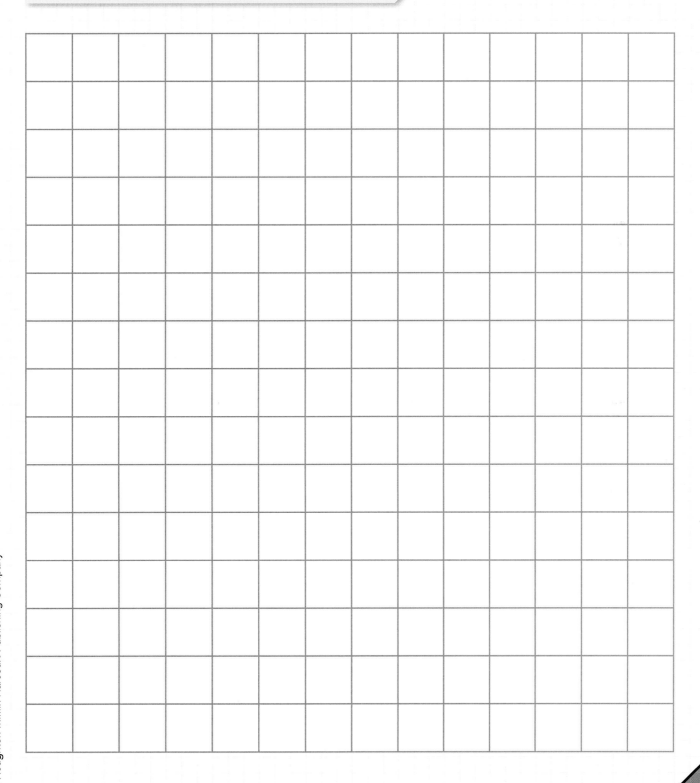

Home Note: Your child uses a growing pattern of 6s to figure out products.

Equations with a Second Factor of 6

➤ Write the missing products and equations.

$1 \times 6 = \boxed{}$

$2 \times 6 = \boxed{}$

$3 \times 6 = \boxed{}$

$4 \times 6 = \boxed{}$

$5 \times 6 = \boxed{}$

$\underline{} \times \underline{} = \boxed{}$

$\underline{} \times \underline{} = \boxed{}$

$\underline{} \times \underline{} = \boxed{}$

$\underline{} \times \underline{} = \boxed{}$

$\underline{} \times \underline{} = \boxed{}$

$\underline{} \times \underline{} = \boxed{}$

$\underline{} \times \underline{} = \boxed{}$

$13 \times 6 = 78$

$14 \times 6 = 84$

$15 \times 6 = \boxed{}$

$16 \times 6 = 96$

$17 \times 6 = 102$

$18 \times 6 = \boxed{}$

$19 \times 6 = 114$

$\underline{} \times \underline{} = \boxed{}$

$21 \times 6 = 126$

$\underline{} \times \underline{} = \boxed{}$

$23 \times 6 = 138$

$\underline{} \times \underline{} = \boxed{}$

Home Note: Your child writes products and equations with a second factor of 6.

Multiples of 6

➤ Color all the multiples of 6 on this chart. Use your products from page 34.

X	1	2	3	4	5	6	7	8	9	10	11	12
1	1	2	3	4	5	6	7	8	9	10	11	12
2	2	4	6	8	10	12	14	16	18	20	22	24
3	3	6	9	12	15	18	21	24	27	30	33	36
4	4	8	12	16	20	24	28	32	36	40	44	48
5	5	10	15	20	25	30	35	40	45	50	55	60
6	6	12	18	24	30	36	42	48	54	60	66	72
7	7	14	21	28	35	42	49	56	63	70	77	84
8	8	16	24	32	40	48	56	64	72	80	88	96
9	9	18	27	36	45	54	63	72	81	90	99	108
10	10	20	30	40	50	60	70	80	90	100	110	120
11	11	22	33	44	55	66	77	88	99	110	121	132
12	12	24	36	48	60	72	84	96	108	120	132	144

Home Note: Your child colors multiples of 6 on a multiplication chart.

Practice Recording Sheet for Pathways

DIRECTIONS

➤ This recording sheet is for a practice game.
➤ Your teacher will take the first turn.
➤ Record your teacher's equations in the first column.
➤ Record students' equations in the second column.

Pathways Game Board Ⓐ

	32	24	15	48
28	40	35	64	20
30	12	56	21	16
9	25	49	42	36

③ 4 5 ⑥ 7 8

Teacher	Students

Home Note: Your child records equations for a practice game of *Pathways*.

Pathways Recording Sheet

HOW TO PLAY

What you need

• *Pathways* Game Board, tiles, dry erase marker

1

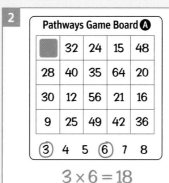

	Pathways Game Board Ⓐ			
■	32	24	15	48
28	40	35	64	20
30	12	56	21	16
9	25	49	42	36

③ 4 5 ⑥ 7 8

Player A marks two factors, and places a green tile on the product.

2

	Pathways Game Board Ⓐ			
■	32	24	15	48
28	40	35	64	20
30	12	56	21	16
9	25	49	42	36

③ 4 5 ⑥ 7 8

$3 \times 6 = 18$

Player B checks that the product is correct. Both players write the equation.

3

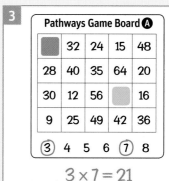

	Pathways Game Board Ⓐ			
■	32	24	15	48
28	40	35	64	20
30	12	56	■	16
9	25	49	42	36

③ 4 5 6 ⑦ 8

$3 \times 7 = 21$

Player B marks one new factor, and places a yellow tile on the product.
Player A checks the product, and both players write the equation.

➤ **The winner is the first player to complete a path from top to bottom or from side to side of the game board.**

Your name:	Your partner's name:

Home Note: Your child records a game of *Pathways*, writing equations for the chosen factors.

Multiples of 5

DIRECTIONS

➤ Write the missing products.

1 × 5 = ☐

2 × 5 = ☐

3 × 5 = ☐

4 × 5 = ☐

5 × 5 = ☐

6 × 5 = ☐

7 × 5 = ☐

8 × 5 = ☐

9 × 5 = ☐

10 × 5 = ☐

11 × 5 = ☐

12 × 5 = ☐

13 × 5 = 65

14 × 5 = ☐

15 × 5 = 75

16 × 5 = ☐

17 × 5 = 85

18 × 5 = 90

19 × 5 = 95

20 × 5 = ☐

21 × 5 = 105

22 × 5 = 110

23 × 5 = 115

24 × 5 = ☐

25 × 5 = 125

26 × 5 = 130

27 × 5 = 135

28 × 5 = 140

Home Note: Your child writes products of equations with a second factor of 5.

Multiples of 5

➤ Color the multiples of 5 on this chart. Use your products from page 38.

X	1	2	3	4	5	6	7	8	9	10	11	12
1	1	2	3	4	5	6	7	8	9	10	11	12
2	2	4	6	8	10	12	14	16	18	20	22	24
3	3	6	9	12	15	18	21	24	27	30	33	36
4	4	8	12	16	20	24	28	32	36	40	44	48
5	5	10	15	20	25	30	35	40	45	50	55	60
6	6	12	18	24	30	36	42	48	54	60	66	72
7	7	14	21	28	35	42	49	56	63	70	77	84
8	8	16	24	32	40	48	56	64	72	80	88	96
9	9	18	27	36	45	54	63	72	81	90	99	108
10	10	20	30	40	50	60	70	80	90	100	110	120
11	11	22	33	44	55	66	77	88	99	110	121	132
12	12	24	36	48	60	72	84	96	108	120	132	144

Home Note: Your child colors multiples of 5 on a multiplication chart.

Multiples of 4

DIRECTIONS

➤ Write the missing products.

$1 \times 4 = \boxed{}$

$2 \times 4 = \boxed{}$

$3 \times 4 = \boxed{}$

$4 \times 4 = \boxed{}$

$5 \times 4 = \boxed{}$

$6 \times 4 = \boxed{}$

$7 \times 4 = \boxed{}$

$8 \times 4 = \boxed{}$

$9 \times 4 = \boxed{}$

$10 \times 4 = \boxed{}$

$11 \times 4 = \boxed{}$

$12 \times 4 = \boxed{}$

$13 \times 4 = 52$

$14 \times 4 = 56$

$15 \times 4 = \boxed{}$

$16 \times 4 = 64$

$17 \times 4 = 68$

$18 \times 4 = \boxed{}$

$19 \times 4 = 76$

$20 \times 4 = \boxed{}$

$21 \times 4 = 84$

$22 \times 4 = 88$

$23 \times 4 = 92$

$24 \times 4 = 96$

$25 \times 4 = \boxed{}$

$26 \times 4 = 104$

$27 \times 4 = 108$

$28 \times 4 = 112$

$29 \times 4 = 116$

$30 \times 4 = \boxed{}$

$31 \times 4 = 124$

$32 \times 4 = 128$

$33 \times 4 = 132$

$34 \times 4 = 136$

$35 \times 4 = \boxed{}$

$36 \times 4 = 144$

Home Note: Your child writes products of equations with a second factor of 4.

Multiples of 4

DIRECTIONS

➤ Color the multiples of 4 on this chart. Use your products from page 40.

X	1	2	3	4	5	6	7	8	9	10	11	12
1	1	2	3	4	5	6	7	8	9	10	11	12
2	2	4	6	8	10	12	14	16	18	20	22	24
3	3	6	9	12	15	18	21	24	27	30	33	36
4	4	8	12	16	20	24	28	32	36	40	44	48
5	5	10	15	20	25	30	35	40	45	50	55	60
6	6	12	18	24	30	36	42	48	54	60	66	72
7	7	14	21	28	35	42	49	56	63	70	77	84
8	8	16	24	32	40	48	56	64	72	80	88	96
9	9	18	27	36	45	54	63	72	81	90	99	108
10	10	20	30	40	50	60	70	80	90	100	110	120
11	11	22	33	44	55	66	77	88	99	110	121	132
12	12	24	36	48	60	72	84	96	108	120	132	144

Home Note: Your child colors multiples of 4 on a multiplication chart.

Multiples of 10

DIRECTIONS

➤ Write the missing products.

$1 \times 10 = \boxed{}$

$2 \times 10 = \boxed{}$

$3 \times 10 = \boxed{}$

$4 \times 10 = \boxed{}$

$5 \times 10 = \boxed{}$

$6 \times 10 = \boxed{}$

$7 \times 10 = \boxed{}$

$8 \times 10 = \boxed{}$

$9 \times 10 = \boxed{}$

$10 \times 10 = \boxed{}$

$11 \times 10 = \boxed{}$

$12 \times 10 = \boxed{}$

$13 \times 10 = 130$

$14 \times 10 = 140$

Home Note: Your child writes products of equations with a second factor of 10.

Multiples of 10

DIRECTIONS

➤ Color the multiples of 10 on this chart. Use your products from page 42.

X	1	2	3	4	5	6	7	8	9	10	11	12
1	1	2	3	4	5	6	7	8	9	10	11	12
2	2	4	6	8	10	12	14	16	18	20	22	24
3	3	6	9	12	15	18	21	24	27	30	33	36
4	4	8	12	16	20	24	28	32	36	40	44	48
5	5	10	15	20	25	30	35	40	45	50	55	60
6	6	12	18	24	30	36	42	48	54	60	66	72
7	7	14	21	28	35	42	49	56	63	70	77	84
8	8	16	24	32	40	48	56	64	72	80	88	96
9	9	18	27	36	45	54	63	72	81	90	99	108
10	10	20	30	40	50	60	70	80	90	100	110	120
11	11	22	33	44	55	66	77	88	99	110	121	132
12	12	24	36	48	60	72	84	96	108	120	132	144

Home Note: Your child colors multiples of 10 on a multiplication chart.

Show What You Know

➤ Complete.

Write equations that have a first factor of 3. Start with 3×1 and go to 3×12.

① ___ $3 \times 1 = 3$ ___   ⑤ _____   ⑨ _____

② _____   ⑥ _____   ⑩ _____

③ _____   ⑦ _____   ⑪ _____

④ _____   ⑧ _____   ⑫ _____

Write the multiples of 6 to 72.

⑬ ___ 6 ___ ___ ___ ___ ___ ___ ___ ___ ___ ___ ___ 72 ___

Color the product of the marked factors and write the matching multiplication equation.

⑭ **Pathways Game Board Ⓐ**

18	32	24	15	48
28	40	35	64	20
30	12	56	21	16
9	25	49	42	36

3 4 ⑤ ⑥ 7 8

⑮ **Pathways Game Board Ⓐ**

18	32	24	15	48
28	40	35	64	20
30	12	56	21	16
9	25	49	42	36

3 ④ 5 ⑥ 7 8

⑯ **Pathways Game Board Ⓐ**

18	32	24	15	48
28	40	35	64	20
30	12	56	21	16
9	25	49	42	36

3 ④ 5 6 ⑦ 8

Equation:

_____

Equation:

_____

Equation:

_____

Home Note: Your child writes equations, skip counts, and finds products.

Equations with Your Assigned Factor

➤ Write equations with a second factor of _____.

_____ × _____ = ☐   _____ × _____ = ☐

_____ × _____ = ☐   _____ × _____ = ☐

_____ × _____ = ☐   _____ × _____ = ☐

_____ × _____ = ☐   _____ × _____ = ☐

_____ × _____ = ☐   _____ × _____ = ☐

_____ × _____ = ☐   _____ × _____ = ☐

_____ × _____ = ☐   _____ × _____ = ☐

_____ × _____ = ☐   _____ × _____ = ☐

_____ × _____ = ☐   _____ × _____ = ☐

_____ × _____ = ☐   _____ × _____ = ☐

Home Note: Your child writes equations for an assigned factor.

Multiples of _____

➤ Color the multiples of _____ on this chart. Use your products from page 45.

X	1	2	3	4	5	6	7	8	9	10	11	12
1	1	2	3	4	5	6	7	8	9	10	11	12
2	2	4	6	8	10	12	14	16	18	20	22	24
3	3	6	9	12	15	18	21	24	27	30	33	36
4	4	8	12	16	20	24	28	32	36	40	44	48
5	5	10	15	20	25	30	35	40	45	50	55	60
6	6	12	18	24	30	36	42	48	54	60	66	72
7	7	14	21	28	35	42	49	56	63	70	77	84
8	8	16	24	32	40	48	56	64	72	80	88	96
9	9	18	27	36	45	54	63	72	81	90	99	108
10	10	20	30	40	50	60	70	80	90	100	110	120
11	11	22	33	44	55	66	77	88	99	110	121	132
12	12	24	36	48	60	72	84	96	108	120	132	144

Home Note: Your child colors multiples of an assigned number.

Equations with Your Own Factor

➤ Write equations with a second factor of _____.

_____ × _____ = ☐   _____ × _____ = ☐

_____ × _____ = ☐   _____ × _____ = ☐

_____ × _____ = ☐   _____ × _____ = ☐

_____ × _____ = ☐   _____ × _____ = ☐

_____ × _____ = ☐   _____ × _____ = ☐

_____ × _____ = ☐   _____ × _____ = ☐

_____ × _____ = ☐   _____ × _____ = ☐

_____ × _____ = ☐   _____ × _____ = ☐

_____ × _____ = ☐   _____ × _____ = ☐

_____ × _____ = ☐   _____ × _____ = ☐

_____ × _____ = ☐   _____ × _____ = ☐

_____ × _____ = ☐   _____ × _____ = ☐

Home Note: Your child writes equations for a factor they choose.

Multiples of ____

➤ This is an extra chart. You can use it to replace a chart that you made a mistake on. Or you can use it to color your products from page 47.

X	1	2	3	4	5	6	7	8	9	10	11	12
1	1	2	3	4	5	6	7	8	9	10	11	12
2	2	4	6	8	10	12	14	16	18	20	22	24
3	3	6	9	12	15	18	21	24	27	30	33	36
4	4	8	12	16	20	24	28	32	36	40	44	48
5	5	10	15	20	25	30	35	40	45	50	55	60
6	6	12	18	24	30	36	42	48	54	60	66	72
7	7	14	21	28	35	42	49	56	63	70	77	84
8	8	16	24	32	40	48	56	64	72	80	88	96
9	9	18	27	36	45	54	63	72	81	90	99	108
10	10	20	30	40	50	60	70	80	90	100	110	120
11	11	22	33	44	55	66	77	88	99	110	121	132
12	12	24	36	48	60	72	84	96	108	120	132	144

Home Note: Your child colors multiples of a number on a multiplication chart.

Bat Squares

➤ Draw squares for the bat arrangements you make with tiles for 2 × 2, 3 × 3, 4 × 4, 5 × 5, and 9 × 9.

➤ Write the multiplication problem inside each square.

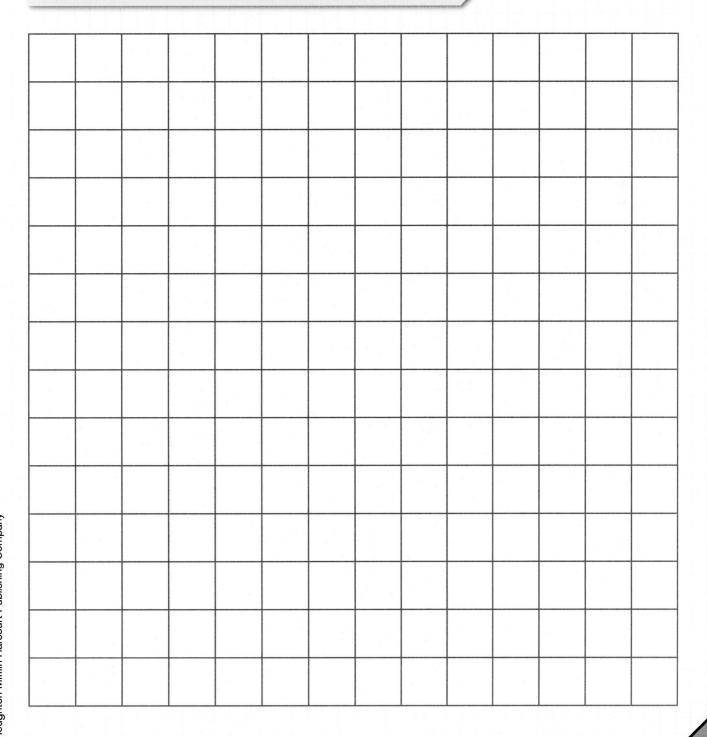

Home Note: Your child builds squares with tiles and records the arrangements, then writes matching equations.

Bat Squares

DIRECTIONS

➤ Draw squares for the bat arrangements you make with tiles for 6 × 6, 7 × 7, and 8 × 8.

➤ Write the multiplication problem inside each square.

© Houghton Mifflin Harcourt Publishing Company

Home Note: Your child builds squares with tiles and
records the arrangements, then writes matching equations.

Bat Squares

➤ Draw a square for the 10 × 10 bat arrangement you make with tiles.

➤ Write the multiplication problem inside the square.

Home Note: Your child builds squares with tiles and records the arrangements, then writes matching equations.

Multiplying by 10

DIRECTIONS

➤ Write the missing products.

1. $1 \times 10 = \boxed{}$

2. $5 \times 10 = \boxed{}$

3. $10 \times 12 = \boxed{}$

4. $7 \times 10 = \boxed{}$

5. $10 \times 3 = \boxed{}$

6. $11 \times 10 = \boxed{}$

7. $10 \times 8 = \boxed{}$

8. $2 \times 10 = \boxed{}$

9. $4 \times 10 = \boxed{}$

10. $9 \times 10 = \boxed{}$

11. $6 \times 10 = \boxed{}$

12. $12 \times 10 = \boxed{}$

13. $10 \times 11 = \boxed{}$

14. $10 \times 5 = \boxed{}$

➤ In the box below, show how you can figure out the product of 6×10.

15. $6 \times 10 = \boxed{}$

Home Note: Your child multiplies with 10 as a factor.

Square Numbers

➤ Use your cut-out squares to find square numbers on the multiplication chart.

➤ Color the square number on the chart for each of your squares.

X	1	2	3	4	5	6	7	8	9	10	11	12
1	1	2	3	4	5	6	7	8	9	10	11	12
2	2	4	6	8	10	12	14	16	18	20	22	24
3	3	6	9	12	15	18	21	24	27	30	33	36
4	4	8	12	16	20	24	28	32	36	40	44	48
5	5	10	15	20	25	30	35	40	45	50	55	60
6	6	12	18	24	30	36	42	48	54	60	66	72
7	7	14	21	28	35	42	49	56	63	70	77	84
8	8	16	24	32	40	48	56	64	72	80	88	96
9	9	18	27	36	45	54	63	72	81	90	99	108
10	10	20	30	40	50	60	70	80	90	100	110	120
11	11	22	33	44	55	66	77	88	99	110	121	132
12	12	24	36	48	60	72	84	96	108	120	132	144

© Houghton Mifflin Harcourt Publishing Company

Home Note: Your child colors square numbers on a multiplication chart.

11 × 11 Square

➤ Draw an 11 × 11 square on the grid.

➤ Draw a line to split the square so that there are two rectangles: 10 × 11 and 1 × 11.

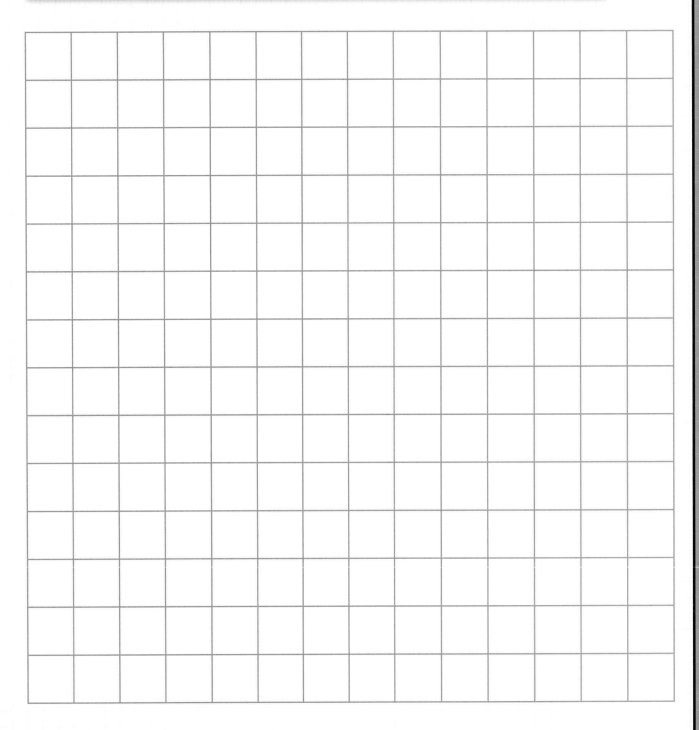

Home Note: Your child draws and splits an 11 × 11 square.

12 × 12 Square

DIRECTIONS

➤ Draw a 12 × 12 square on the grid.

➤ Draw a line to split the square so that there are two rectangles: 10 × 12 and 2 × 12.

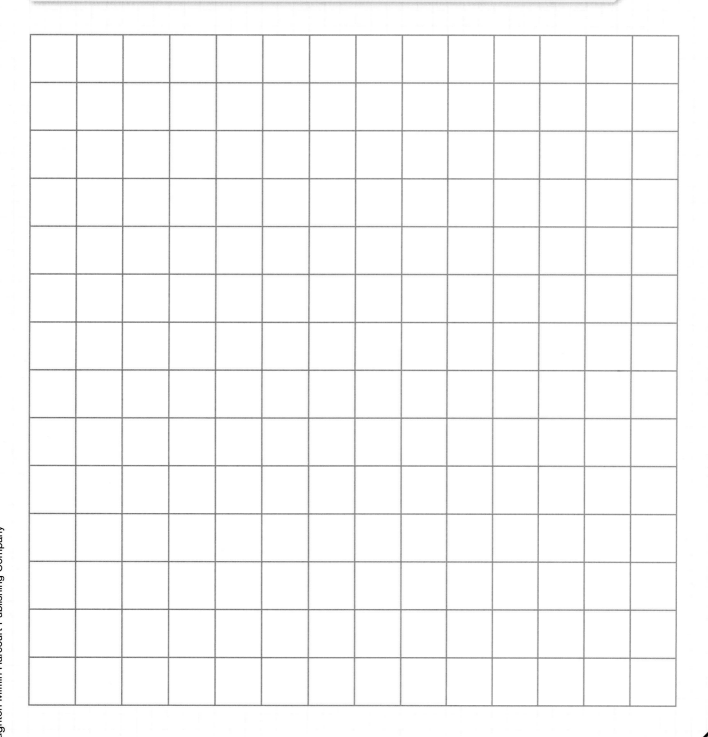

Home Note: Your child draws and splits a 12 × 12 square.

Show What You Know

➤ Write a multiplication equation that shows the number is a square number. You may use your cut-out squares to help you.

① 4 _____

② 25 _____

③ 64 _____

➤ Use the square to solve problems 4 and 5.

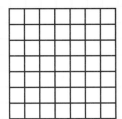

④ What is the square number for this square? _____

⑤ Write a multiplication equation for the square. _____

➤ Write the products.

⑥ 10 × 5 = ☐

⑦ 10 × 11 = ☐

⑧ 10 × 12 = ☐

⑨ 10 × 10 = ☐

⑩ 11 × 10 = ☐

⑪ 9 × 10 = ☐

⑫ 6 × 10 = ☐

Home Note: Your child writes equations for square numbers and writes products with a factor of 10.

Show What You Know

DIRECTIONS

➤ Write the missing square numbers. You may use your cut-out squares to help you.

➤ Shade each of the other square numbers.

✕	1	2	3	4	5	6	7	8	9	10	11	12
1	1	2	3	4	5	6	7	8	9	10	11	12
2	2	4	6	8	10	12	14	16	18	20	22	24
3	3	6		12	15	18	21	24	27	30	33	36
4	4	8	12	16	20	24	28	32	36	40	44	48
5	5	10	15	20	25	30	35	40	45	50	55	60
6	6	12	18	24	30		42	48	54	60	66	72
7	7	14	21	28	35	42	49	56	63	70	77	84
8	8	16	24	32	40	48	56	64	72	80	88	96
9	9	18	27	36	45	54	63	72		90	99	108
10	10	20	30	40	50	60	70	80	90	100	110	120
11	11	22	33	44	55	66	77	88	99	110	121	132
12	12	24	36	48	60	72	84	96	108	120	132	

Home Note: Your child writes products that are square numbers on a multiplication chart.

Pathways Recording Sheet

HOW TO PLAY

What you need

• *Pathways* Game Board, tiles, dry erase marker

1

Pathways Game Board Ⓐ

	32	24	15	48
28	40	35	64	20
30	12	56	21	16
9	25	49	42	36

③ 4 5 ⑥ 7 8

Player A marks two factors, and places a green tile on the product.

2

Pathways Game Board Ⓐ

	32	24	15	48
28	40	35	64	20
30	12	56	21	16
9	25	49	42	36

③ 4 5 ⑥ 7 8

$3 \times 6 = 18$

Player B checks that the product is correct. Both players write the equation.

3

Pathways Game Board Ⓐ

	32	24	15	48
28	40	35	64	20
30	12	56		16
9	25	49	42	36

③ 4 5 6 ⑦ 8

$3 \times 7 = 21$

Player B marks one new factor, and places a yellow tile on the product.
Player A checks the product, and both players write the equation.

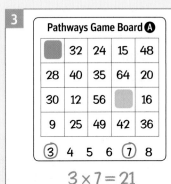

➤ **The winner is the first player to complete a path from top to bottom or from side to side of the game board.**

Your name:	Your partner's name:

Home Note: Your child records a game of *Pathways*.

Cross Out Products

DIRECTIONS

➤ Draw a line through the products that are easy for you to figure out or remember.

➤ Draw a line through the products you know.

➤ Draw a line through products that are the same because of the Commutative Property.

➤ Circle the remaining products.

X	1	2	3	4	5	6	7	8	9	10	11	12
1	1	2	3	4	5	6	7	8	9	10	11	12
2	2	4	6	8	10	12	14	16	18	20	22	24
3	3	6	9	12	15	18	21	24	27	30	33	36
4	4	8	12	16	20	24	28	32	36	40	44	48
5	5	10	15	20	25	30	35	40	45	50	55	60
6	6	12	18	24	30	36	42	48	54	60	66	72
7	7	14	21	28	35	42	49	56	63	70	77	84
8	8	16	24	32	40	48	56	64	72	80	88	96
9	9	18	27	36	45	54	63	72	81	90	99	108
10	10	20	30	40	50	60	70	80	90	100	110	120
11	11	22	33	44	55	66	77	88	99	110	121	132
12	12	24	36	48	60	72	84	96	108	120	132	144

Home Note: Your child crosses out products on a multiplication chart.

Multiplication Facts to Learn

DIRECTIONS

➤ Choose ten of the circled products from your chart on page 61.

➤ Write equations for the ten products.

➤ Practice them during the week.

➤ When you learn a fact, cross it off and write a new one.

1. _____

2. _____

3. _____

4. _____

5. _____

6. _____

7. _____

8. _____

9. _____

10. _____

Home Note: Your child writes equations for products they need to learn.

Pathways Recording Sheet

HOW TO PLAY

What you need

• *Pathways* Game Board, tiles, dry erase marker

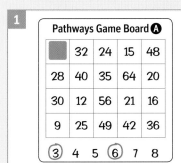

1

Player A marks two factors, and places a green tile on the product.

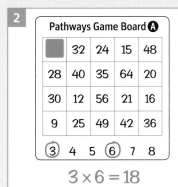

2

$3 \times 6 = 18$

Player B checks that the product is correct. Both players write the equation.

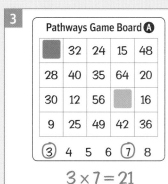

3

$3 \times 7 = 21$

Player B marks one new factor, and places a yellow tile on the product.

Player A checks the product, and both players write the equation.

➤ **The winner is the first player to complete a path from top to bottom or from side to side of the game board.**

Your name:	Your partner's name:

Home Note: Your child records a game of *Pathways*.

Products for Problems with Factors of 9

➤ Write the products.

① 1 × 9 = ☐

② 2 × 9 = ☐

③ 3 × 9 = ☐

④ 4 × 9 = ☐

⑤ 5 × 9 = ☐

⑥ 6 × 9 = ☐

⑦ 7 × 9 = ☐

⑧ 8 × 9 = ☐

⑨ 9 × 9 = ☐

⑩ 10 × 9 = ☐

⑪ 11 × 9 = ☐

⑫ 12 × 9 = ☐

➤ Explain how you would figure out 13 × 9. Write the equation.

⑬

Home Note: Your child writes products for problems with factors of 9.

Show What You Know

➤ Write the products from memory or by figuring them out.

➤ Do not use a multiplication chart to help you.

① 3 × 3 = ☐

② 6 × 3 = ☐

③ 12 × 3 = ☐

④ 2 × 9 = ☐

⑤ 4 × 9 = ☐

⑥ 8 × 9 = ☐

⑦ 11 × 7 = ☐

⑧ 5 × 8 = ☐

⑨ 10 × 8 = ☐

⑩ 12 × 0 = ☐

⑪ 9 × 6 = ☐

⑫ 9 × 7 = ☐

⑬ 7 × 3 = ☐

⑭ 7 × 6 = ☐

⑮ 6 × 6 = ☐

⑯ 12 × 6 = ☐

⑰ 4 × 4 = ☐

⑱ 8 × 4 = ☐

⑲ 8 × 8 = ☐

⑳ 7 × 4 = ☐

➤ Write the products. Answer the question.

㉑ 8 × 3 = 24   3 × 8 = ☐

㉒ 9 × 5 = 45   5 × 9 = ☐

㉓ 8 × 6 = 48   6 × 8 = ☐

㉔ 1 × 12 = 12   12 × 1 = ☐

㉕ How can you use the *Commutative Property of Multiplication* to solve ㉑ to ㉔?

_____

_____

Home Note: Your child uses patterns to help write products of equations.

Multiplication

➤ Tell about multiplication with words, numbers, and pictures.

ABOUT MULTIPLICATION

Lesson 26

Home Note: Your child writes about multiplication.

Rectangle Splitting: 11 × 8

➤ Show how you can figure out the product by splitting the rectangle.

11 × 8 = ☐

Home Note: Your child splits an 11 × 8 rectangle to find the product.

Lesson 27

67

Number Splitting: 11

DIRECTIONS

Problem

11×12

1 Split a factor and write two equations.

$$11 = 10 + 1$$
$$10 \times 12 = 120$$
$$1 \times 12 = 12$$

2 Add the products of the two equations.

$$120 + 12 = 132$$

3 Write the product for the problem.

$$11 \times 12 = \boxed{132}$$

---

① 11×14

Equation 1 _____

Equation 2 _____

Add the products.

_____

Write the product. $11 \times 14 = \boxed{}$

---

② 11×17

Equation 1 _____

Equation 2 _____

Add the products.

_____

Write the product. $11 \times 17 = \boxed{}$

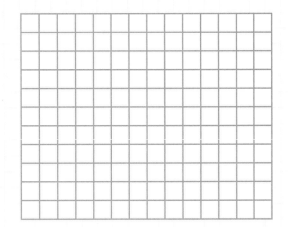

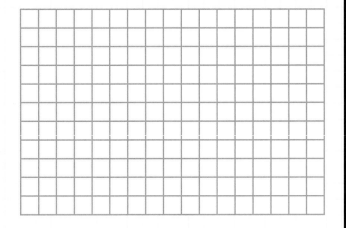

Home Note: Your child splits the factor 11 to find products.

Rectangle Splitting: 12 × 6

➤ Show how you can figure out the product by splitting the rectangle.

$12 \times 6 = \boxed{}$

© Houghton Mifflin Harcourt Publishing Company

Home Note: Your child splits a 12 × 6 rectangle to find the product.

Number Splitting: 12

DIRECTIONS

➤ Write two equations for each problem.

➤ Add the products.

➤ Write the product of the original problem.

➤ Do Problem 1 as your teacher writes the equations on the board.

① 12 × 15

Equation 1 _____

Equation 2 _____

Add the products.

_____

Write the product.   12 × 15 = ☐

③ 12 × 16

Equation 1 _____

Equation 2 _____

Add the products.

_____

Write the product.   12 × 16 = ☐

② 12 × 14

Equation 1 _____

Equation 2 _____

Add the products.

_____

Write the product.   12 × 14 = ☐

Home Note: Your child splits the factor 12 to find products.

Number Splitting with a Factor of 12

DIRECTIONS

1 Write the product from memory if you can.

$12 \times 2 = \boxed{24}$

2 Show that the product is correct using number splitting.

$10 \times 2 = 20$
$2 \times 2 = 4$
$20 + 4 = 24$

3 If you don't know the product, use number splitting to figure the product.

$12 \times 15 = \boxed{?}$

$10 \times 15 = 150$
$2 \times 15 = 30$
$150 + 30 = 180$
$12 \times 15 = 180$

① $12 \times 3 = \boxed{}$

④ $12 \times 6 = \boxed{}$

⑦ $12 \times 9 = \boxed{}$

② $12 \times 4 = \boxed{}$

⑤ $12 \times 7 = \boxed{}$

⑧ $12 \times 11 = \boxed{}$

③ $12 \times 5 = \boxed{}$

⑥ $12 \times 8 = \boxed{}$

⑨ $12 \times 12 = \boxed{}$

Home Note: Your child uses number splitting to find products of problems with a factor of 12.

Show What You Know

➤ Write the products.

① 12 × 12 = ☐

② 11 × 7 = ☐

③ 11 × 10 = ☐

④ 11 × 12 = ☐

⑤ 12 × 10 = ☐

⑥ 12 × 5 = ☐

⑦ 12 × 11 = ☐

⑧ 11 × 13 = ☐

➤ Use the number-splitting strategy to find the product. Write each equation.

⑨ 12 × 13

_____

_____

_____

_____

Home Note: Your child writes products from memory or by using the number-splitting strategy.

Show What You Know

DIRECTIONS

➤ **Write the products.**

① $3 \times 3 =$ ☐

② $3 \times 6 =$ ☐

③ $4 \times 4 =$ ☐

④ $8 \times 7 =$ ☐

⑤ $6 \times 0 =$ ☐

⑥ $6 \times 8 =$ ☐

⑦ $12 \times 2 =$ ☐

⑧ $2 \times 12 =$ ☐

⑨ $12 \times 8 =$ ☐

⑩ $6 \times 6 =$ ☐

⑪ $6 \times 12 =$ ☐

⑫ $12 \times 6 =$ ☐

⑬ $7 \times 6 =$ ☐

⑭ $7 \times 12 =$ ☐

⑮ $8 \times 4 =$ ☐

⑯ $8 \times 8 =$ ☐

⑰ $8 \times 5 =$ ☐

⑱ $8 \times 10 =$ ☐

⑲ $9 \times 4 =$ ☐

⑳ $9 \times 8 =$ ☐

㉑ $9 \times 3 =$ ☐

㉒ $9 \times 6 =$ ☐

㉓ $12 \times 3 =$ ☐

㉔ $7 \times 3 =$ ☐

㉕ $12 \times 12 =$ ☐

㉖ $9 \times 9 =$ ☐

㉗ $10 \times 10 =$ ☐

㉘ $11 \times 4 =$ ☐

㉙ $11 \times 8 =$ ☐

㉚ $7 \times 7 =$ ☐

Home Note: Your child writes products from memory or by using any strategy.

Math Vocabulary

Home Note: Your child reinforces understanding of math vocabulary as he or she records terms and examples.

Glossary

Commutative Property of Multiplication

Changing the order of factors does not change the product. This is called the *Commutative Property of Multiplication*.

An example of this property is, 3 × 5 = 5 × 3.

equal

Equal means the same amount. For example, twelve is equal to three times four. The symbol for *equal* is =.

equal groups

In *equal groups*, each group has the same amount. For example, if there are circles and each circle has 2 stars, then the stars are in *equal groups*.

equation

An *equation* is a number sentence that uses an equal sign to show that two amounts have the same value. For example, 3 + 4 = 7, 3 × 4 = 12, 5 − 0 = 5 are *equations*.

factor

Factors are numbers that you multiply to get a product. For example, 3 and 7 are *factors* in the equation 3 × 7 = 21.

multiple

Multiples of a number are numbers that you get when multiplying that number by 1, 2, 3, 4, 5, and so on.

For example, *multiples* of 5 are 5, 10, 15, 20, 25 because 5 × 1 = 5, 5 × 2 = 10, 5 × 3 = 15, 5 × 4 = 20, 5 × 5 = 25.

multiplication

Multiplication is what you do when you find the total number of items in equal groups.

multiplication equation

A *multiplication equation* is a number sentence with an equal sign and a times sign. What is on the left side of the equal sign equals what is on the right side. Examples of *multiplication equations* are 18 = 6 × 3 and 6 × 3 = 18.

Multiplication Property of One

The product of any number and 1 is the number. For example, 7 × 1 and 1 × 7 both equal 7.

multiply

Multiply is what you do when you find the product of factors. For example, if you *multiply* 5 and 2, you get the product 10.